Patriotic Penmanship

for
Grade 7 and 8
Book II

by Mary Ellen Tedrow-Wynn

About the Author

Mary Ellen Tedrow-Wynn

is the mother of seven children and has been schooling at home for more than 25 years. Helping others find appropriate, affordable books has been her love since she began the journey herself. You can contact her with questions or comments at the website listed below.

Note from the author and publisher:

I hope you will be blessed by the words we have presented to you. While writing, may your student take in character-building thoughts. And maybe, just maybe, he or she will also say and write great things!

These books are meant to be written in and are therefore considered consumable. Please purchase a copy for each child. We are working hard to keep the price affordable. You can help us do this by paying for what you use. Character begins at home.

We love to hear from you. We have checked the book for errors. However, should you notice any that we have missed, please do reach out to us via the email address below. Comments and suggestions are most welcome.

Schools and co-ops: Please contact us for special pricing.

Find this and our other great books here:

www.laurelwoodbooks.com

marylnw7@gmail.com

Laurelwood Books
1639 Ebenezer Road
Bluemont, VA 20135

Using Patriotic Penmanship

At the beginning of the week read the full quote to the student. Assign the quantity of work based on your child's capabilities. Each lesson equals one week's work. As with all handwriting, student should be seated with feet touching the floor, and arms resting comfortably on the table. Pencil should be sharp and gripped firmly. Keep in mind that too tight a grip can cause fatigue and pain. Instruct children to leave a "finger space" between each word. Teacher/parent, please realize that each person develops his/her own style of handwriting. As the student "learns", give some leeway to their creativity.

Patriotic Penmanship can be used to learn and practice handwriting but it can be much more. You decide! Throughout all the grade levels we have incorporated great quotes, verses, poems, and hymns. Study the great men and women from the past. Find out what drove them to say and/or write these things. Was it a war, a death, a connection with the Lord? Delve into rich history with your sons and/or daughters. These words can open the door for great conversations. "What do you think about this?" "What was happening in the world?" "Find out more about the writer." "Do you agree with this quote?" "Why? Or Why not?"

What people are saying about Patriotic Penmanship:

"Another winner by Mary Ellen." (K. Schatz, homeschooling mother)

"LOVE THEM!!!! I would use these! In fact I wish I had had them for my kids. I love the quotes--I think if I was using these to teach, I would go on to have the student copy the FULL quote from the little note card as well! Then we could look up the person and/or situation for the quote and go on from there. Maybe suggest these as jumping-off points for further study. Great idea!" (L. Brown, homeschool mom of four grown kids)

"I love how this is presented. Can I pre-order? I want these for my three children." (H. Fontaine, homeschooling mother)

"What a great project!! I looked over the 2nd grade one and I really like the structure. Consistent short lessons to keep up practice…really awesome quotes! A second grade Patriotic Penmanship would mesh quite nicely with My Father's World curriculum for 2nd and 3rd graders; it focuses on America. Blessings to you." (C. Hoffman)

"What a treasure! My children are able to learn handwriting with profound insights from our nation's rich history, so much more than a handwriting curriculum." (Canyon)

Practice Time!

Aa Aa

Bb Bb

Cc Cc

Dd Dd

Ee Ee

Ff Ff

Gg Gg

Hh Hh

Ii Ii

Jj Jj

Kk Kk

Ll Ll

Mm Mm

Aa Bb Cc Dd Ee Ff Gg Hh Ii Jj Kk Ll Mm

Practice Time!

Nn Nn

Oo Oo

Pp Pp

Qq Qq

Rr Rr

Ss Ss

Tt Tt

Uu Uu

Vv Vv

Ww Ww

Xx Xx

Yy Yy

Zz Zz

Now lets' get started!

Nn Oo Pp Qq Rr Ss Tt Uu Vv Ww Xx Yy Zz

Lesson 1

Name: _____

My dream is of a place and a time where America will once again be seen as the last best hope of earth.

Abraham Lincoln

My dream is of a place and a time where America will once again be seen as the last best hope of earth.

✎ Tracing Practice

Trace the quote twice.

My dream is of a place and a time where America will once again be seen as the last best hope of earth.

My dream is of a place and a time where America will once again be seen as the last best hope of earth.

Aa Bb Cc Dd Ee Ff Gg Hh Ii Jj Kk Ll Mm

✏️ Writing Practice

Trace the quote and write it underneath.

My dream is of a place and a time

where America will once again be

seen as the last best hope of earth.

✏️ Full Quote

Write the full quote twice. The first word of each line of the quote is provided.

My

where

seen

My

where

seen

Nearly all men can stand adversity, but if you want to test a man's character, give him power.

Abraham Lincoln

Nearly all men can stand adversity,

but if you want to test a man's

character, give him power.

✎ Tracing Practice

Trace the quote twice.

Nearly all men can stand adversity,

but if you want to test a man's

character, give him power.

Nearly all men can stand adversity,

but if you want to test a man's

character, give him power.

Aa Bb Cc Dd Ee Ff Gg Hh Ii Jj Kk Ll Mm

✎ Writing Practice

Trace the quote and write it underneath.

Nearly all men can stand adversity,

but if you want to test a man's

character, give him power.

✎ Full Quote

Write the full quote twice. The first word of each line of the quote is provided.

Nearly

but

character

Nearly

but

character

Lesson 3

> Peace cannot be kept by force;
> it can only be achieved by understanding.
>
> Albert Einstein

Peace cannot be kept by force

it can only be achieved

by understanding.

🖊 Tracing Practice

Trace the quote twice.

Peace cannot be kept by force

it can only be achieved

by understanding.

Peace cannot be kept by force

it can only be achieved

by understanding.

10   Aa   Bb   Cc   Dd   Ee   Ff   Gg   Hh   Ii   Jj   Kk   Ll   Mm

✎ Writing Practice

Trace the quote and write it underneath.

Peace cannot be kept by force

it can only be achieved

by understanding.

✎ Full Quote

Write the full quote twice. The first word of each line of the quote is provided.

Peace

it

by

Peace

it

by

Nn Oo Pp Qq Rr Ss Tt Uu Vv Ww Xx Yy Zz   *11*

Lesson 4

Name: _____

> *Gratitude makes sense of our past,*
> *brings peace for today, and creates a vision for tomorrow.*
>
> *Melody Beattie*

Gratitude makes sense of our past,

brings peace for today,

and creates a vision for tomorrow.

✎ Tracing Practice

Trace the quote twice.

Gratitude makes sense of our past,

brings peace for today,

and creates a vision for tomorrow.

Gratitude makes sense of our past,

brings peace for today,

and creates a vision for tomorrow.

Aa Bb Cc Dd Ee Ff Gg Hh Ii Jj Kk Ll Mm

Writing Practice

Trace the quote and write it underneath.

Gratitude makes sense of our past,

brings peace for today,

and creates a vision for tomorrow.

Full Quote

Write the full quote twice. The first word of each line of the quote is provided.

Gratitude

brings

and

Gratitude

brings

and

Nn Oo Pp Qq Rr Ss Tt Uu Vv Ww Xx Yy Zz

I must trust that the little bit of love that I sow now will bear many fruits, here in this world and the life to come.

Henri Nouwen

I must trust that the little bit of love that I sow now will bear many fruits, here in this world and the life to come.

✎ Tracing Practice

Trace the quote twice.

I must trust that the little bit of love that I sow now will bear many fruits, here in this world and the life to come.

I must trust that the little bit of love that I sow now will bear many fruits, here in this world and the life to come.

Aa Bb Cc Dd Ee Ff Gg Hh Ii Jj Kk Ll Mm

✎ Writing Practice

Trace the quote and write it underneath.

I must trust that the little bit of love

that I sow now will bear many fruits,

here in this world and the life to come.

✎ Full Quote

Write the full quote twice. The first word of each line of the quote is provided.

I

that

here

I

that

here

Lesson 6

Remember that the happiest people are not those getting more, but those giving more.

H. Jackson Brown, Jr.

Remember that the happiest people
are not those getting more,
but those giving more.

✎ Tracing Practice

Trace the quote twice.

Remember that the happiest people
are not those getting more,
but those giving more.

Remember that the happiest people
are not those getting more,
but those giving more.

Aa Bb Cc Dd Ee Ff Gg Hh Ii Jj Kk Ll Mm

✎ Writing Practice

Trace the quote and write it underneath.

Remember that the happiest people

are not those getting more,

but those giving more.

✎ Full Quote

Write the full quote twice. The first word of each line of the quote is provided.

Remember

are

but

Remember

are

but

Insanity: doing the same thing
over and over again and expecting different results.
Unknown

Insanity: doing the same thing

over and over again

and expecting different results.

✎ Tracing Practice

Trace the quote twice.

Insanity: doing the same thing

over and over again

and expecting different results.

Insanity: doing the same thing

over and over again

and expecting different results.

Aa Bb Cc Dd Ee Ff Gg Hh Ii Jj Kk Ll Mm

✎ Writing Practice

Trace the quote and write it underneath.

Insanity: doing the same thing

over and over again

and expecting different results.

✎ Full Quote

Write the full quote twice. The first word of each line of the quote is provided.

Insanity

over

and

Insanity

over

and

> We cannot solve our problems with the same thinking
> we used when we created them.
> Albert Einstein

We cannot solve our problems

with the same thinking we used

when we created them.

✎ Tracing Practice

Trace the quote twice.

We cannot solve our problems

with the same thinking we used

when we created them.

We cannot solve our problems

with the same thinking we used

when we created them.

Aa Bb Cc Dd Ee Ff Gg Hh Ii Jj Kk Ll Mm

✎ Writing Practice

Trace the quote and write it underneath.

We cannot solve our problems

with the same thinking we used

when we created them.

✎ Full Quote

Write the full quote twice. The first word of each line of the quote is provided.

We

with

when

We

with

when

Name: _____

Try not to become a man of success,
but rather try to become a man of value.

Albert Einstein

Try not to become a man
of success, but rather try
to become a man of value.

✎ Tracing Practice

Trace the quote twice.

Try not to become a man
of success, but rather try
to become a man of value.

Try not to become a man
of success, but rather try
to become a man of value.

Aa Bb Cc Dd Ee Ff Gg Hh Ii Jj Kk Ll Mm

✎ Writing Practice

Trace the quote and write it underneath.

Try not to become a man

of success, but rather try

to become a man of value.

✎ Full Quote

Write the full quote twice. The first word of each line of the quote is provided.

Try

of

to

Try

of

to

Lesson 10

Name: _____

To survive in peace and harmony, united and strong,
we must have one people, one nation, one flag.

Pauline Hanson

To survive in peace and harmony,
united and strong, we must have
one people, one nation, one flag.

✏ Tracing Practice

Trace the quote twice.

To survive in peace and harmony,
united and strong, we must have
one people, one nation, one flag.

To survive in peace and harmony,
united and strong, we must have
one people, one nation, one flag.

Aa Bb Cc Dd Ee Ff Gg Hh Ii Jj Kk Ll Mm

Writing Practice

Trace the quote and write it underneath.

To survive in peace and harmony,

united and strong, we must have

one people, one nation, one flag.

Full Quote

Write the full quote twice. The first word of each line of the quote is provided.

To

united

one

To

united

one

A friend is someone who gives you
total freedom to be yourself.

Jim Morrison

A friend is someone
who gives you total freedom
to be yourself.

✎ Tracing Practice

Trace the quote twice.

A friend is someone
who gives you total freedom
to be yourself.

A friend is someone
who gives you total freedom
to be yourself.

Aa Bb Cc Dd Ee Ff Gg Hh Ii Jj Kk Ll Mm

✎ Writing Practice

Trace the quote and write it underneath.

A friend is someone

who gives you total freedom

to be yourself.

✎ Full Quote

Write the full quote twice. The first word of each line of the quote is provided.

A

who

to

A

who

to

Lesson 12

Love is the only force capable
of transforming an enemy into a friend.

Martin Luther King, Jr.

Love is the only force
capable of transforming
an enemy into a friend.

✎ Tracing Practice

Trace the quote twice.

Love is the only force
capable of transforming
an enemy into a friend.

Love is the only force
capable of transforming
an enemy into a friend.

Aa Bb Cc Dd Ee Ff Gg Hh Ii Jj Kk Ll Mm

✎ Writing Practice

Trace the quote and write it underneath.

Love is the only force

capable of transforming

an enemy into a friend.

✎ Full Quote

Write the full quote twice. The first word of each line of the quote is provided.

Love

capable

an

Love

capable

an

Name: _____

> Our character is what we do
> when we think no one is looking.
>
> H. Jackson Brown, Jr.

Our character is what we do

when we think

no one is looking.

✎ Tracing Practice

Trace the quote twice.

Our character is what we do

when we think

no one is looking.

Our character is what we do

when we think

no one is looking.

Aa Bb Cc Dd Ee Ff Gg Hh Ii Jj Kk Ll Mm

✎ Writing Practice

Trace the quote and write it underneath.

Our character is what we do

when we think

no one is looking.

✎ Full Quote

Write the full quote twice. The first word of each line of the quote is provided.

Our

when

no

Our

when

no

Name:_____

Always do your best. What you plant now,
you will harvest later.

Og Mandino

Always do your best.

What you plant now,

you will harvest later.

✎ Tracing Practice

Trace the quote twice.

Always do your best.

What you plant now,

you will harvest later.

Always do your best.

What you plant now,

you will harvest later.

Aa Bb Cc Dd Ee Ff Gg Hh Ii Jj Kk Ll Mm

✎ Writing Practice

Trace the quote and write it underneath.

Always do your best.

What you plant now,

you will harvest later.

✎ Full Quote

Write the full quote twice. The first word of each line of the quote is provided.

Always

What

you

Always

What

you

Better to remain silent and be thought a fool
than to speak out and remove all doubt.

Unknown

Better to remain silent and be
thought a fool than to speak out
and remove all doubt.

✎ Tracing Practice

Trace the quote twice.

Better to remain silent and be
thought a fool than to speak out
and remove all doubt.

Better to remain silent and be
thought a fool than to speak out
and remove all doubt.

Aa Bb Cc Dd Ee Ff Gg Hh Ii Jj Kk Ll Mm

✎ Writing Practice

Trace the quote and write it underneath.

Better to remain silent and be

thought a fool than to speak out

and remove all doubt.

✎ Full Quote

Write the full quote twice. The first word of each line of the quote is provided.

Better

thought

and

Better

thought

and

Lesson 16

Success is not final, failure is not fatal:
it is the courage to continue that counts.

Winston Churchill

Success is not final, failure
is not fatal: it is the courage
to continue that counts.

Tracing Practice

Trace the quote twice.

Success is not final, failure
is not fatal: it is the courage
to continue that counts.

Success is not final, failure
is not fatal: it is the courage
to continue that counts.

Aa Bb Cc Dd Ee Ff Gg Hh Ii Jj Kk Ll Mm

✎ Writing Practice

Trace the quote and write it underneath.

Success is not final, failure

is not fatal: it is the courage

to continue that counts.

✎ Full Quote

Write the full quote twice. The first word of each line of the quote is provided.

Success

is

to

Success

is

to

Name: _____

> Coming together is a beginning; keeping together is progress;
> working together is success.
>
> Henry Ford

Coming together is a beginning;

keeping together is progress;

working together is success.

✎ Tracing Practice

Trace the quote twice.

Coming together is a beginning;

keeping together is progress;

working together is success.

Coming together is a beginning;

keeping together is progress;

working together is success.

Aa Bb Cc Dd Ee Ff Gg Hh Ii Jj Kk Ll Mm

✎ Writing Practice

Trace the quote and write it underneath.

Coming together is a beginning;

keeping together is progress;

working together is success.

✎ Full Quote

Write the full quote twice. The first word of each line of the quote is provided.

Coming

keeping

working

Coming

keeping

working

Lesson 18

> *Perfection is not attainable,*
> *but if we chase perfection we can catch excellence.*
>
> *Vince Lombardi*

Perfection is not attainable,

but if we chase perfection

we can catch excellence.

✎ Tracing Practice

Trace the quote twice.

Perfection is not attainable,

but if we chase perfection

we can catch excellence.

Perfection is not attainable,

but if we chase perfection

we can catch excellence.

Aa Bb Cc Dd Ee Ff Gg Hh Ii Jj Kk Ll Mm

✎ Writing Practice

Trace the quote and write it underneath.

Perfection is not attainable,

but if we chase perfection

we can catch excellence.

✎ Full Quote

Write the full quote twice. The first word of each line of the quote is provided.

Perfection

but

we

Perfection

but

we

Name: _____

Live so that when your children think of fairness,
caring, and integrity, they think of you.

H. Jackson Brown, Jr.

Live so that when your children
think of fairness, caring, and integrity,
they think of you.

✎ Tracing Practice

Trace the quote twice.

Live so that when your children
think of fairness, caring, and integrity,
they think of you.

Live so that when your children
think of fairness, caring, and integrity,
they think of you.

Aa Bb Cc Dd Ee Ff Gg Hh Ii Jj Kk Ll Mm

✎ Writing Practice

Trace the quote and write it underneath.

Live so that when your children

think of fairness, caring, and integrity,

they think of you.

✎ Full Quote

Write the full quote twice. The first word of each line of the quote is provided.

Live

think

they

Live

think

they

Lesson 20

Name:_____

It is easier to build strong children
than to repair broken men.

Frederick Douglass

It is easier to build

strong children than

to repair broken men.

✎ Tracing Practice

Trace the quote twice.

It is easier to build

strong children than

to repair broken men.

It is easier to build

strong children than

to repair broken men.

44 Aa Bb Cc Dd Ee Ff Gg Hh Ii Jj Kk Ll Mm

Writing Practice

Trace the quote and write it underneath.

It is easier to build

strong children than

to repair broken men.

Full Quote

Write the full quote twice. The first word of each line of the quote is provided.

It

strong

to

It

strong

to

Lesson 21

Name: _____

> If we ever forget that we are One Nation Under God,
> then we will be a nation gone under.
>
> Ronald Reagan

If we ever forget that we are

One Nation Under God,

then we will be a nation gone under.

✏️ Tracing Practice

Trace the quote twice.

If we ever forget that we are

One Nation Under God,

then we will be a nation gone under.

If we ever forget that we are

One Nation Under God,

then we will be a nation gone under.

46   Aa Bb Cc Dd Ee Ff Gg Hh Ii Jj Kk Ll Mm

✎ Writing Practice

Trace the quote and write it underneath.

If we ever forget that we are

One Nation Under God,

then we will be a nation gone under.

✎ Full Quote

Write the full quote twice. The first word of each line of the quote is provided.

If

One

then

If

One

then

Lesson 22

Every human has four endowments – self-awareness, conscience, independent will, and creative imagination.

Stephen Covey

Every human has four endowments –
self-awareness, conscience, independent
will, and creative imagination.

✎ Tracing Practice

Trace the quote twice.

Every human has four endowments ---
self--awareness, conscience, independent
will, and creative imagination.

Every human has four endowments ---
self--awareness, conscience, independent
will, and creative imagination.

48   Aa   Bb   Cc   Dd   Ee   Ff   Gg   Hh   Ii   Jj   Kk   Ll   Mm

✎ Writing Practice

Trace the quote and write it underneath.

Every human has four endowments --

self--awareness, conscience, independent

will, and creative imagination.

✎ Full Quote

Write the full quote twice. The first word of each line of the quote is provided.

Every

self---

will,

Every

self---

will,

Lesson 23

> Life is ten percent what happens to you
> and ninety percent how you react to it.
>
> Charles R. Swindoll

Life is ten percent what happens
to you and ninety percent
how you react to it.

✎ Tracing Practice

Trace the quote twice.

Life is ten percent what happens
to you and ninety percent
how you react to it.

Life is ten percent what happens
to you and ninety percent
how you react to it.

Aa Bb Cc Dd Ee Ff Gg Hh Ii Jj Kk Ll Mm

✎ Writing Practice

Trace the quote and write it underneath.

Life is ten percent what happens

to you and ninety percent

how you react to it.

✎ Full Quote

Write the full quote twice. The first word of each line of the quote is provided.

Life

to

how

Life

to

how

Lesson 24

Name:_____

Intoxicated with unbroken success, we have become too self-suf-ficient to feel the necessity of redeeming and preserving grace, too proud to pray to the God that made us.

Abraham Lincoln's 1863 Thanksgiving Proclamation

Intoxicated with unbroken success, we have become too self-sufficient to feel the necessity of redeeming and preserving grace, too proud to pray to the God that made us.

✏️ Tracing Practice

Trace the quote twice.

Intoxicated with unbroken success, we have become too self-sufficient to feel the necessity of redeeming and preserving grace, too proud to pray to the God that made us.

Intoxicated with unbroken success, we have become too self-sufficient to feel the necessity of redeeming and preserving grace, too proud to pray to the God that made us.

Aa Bb Cc Dd Ee Ff Gg Hh Ii Jj Kk Ll Mm

✎ Writing Practice

Trace the quote and write it underneath.

Intoxicated with unbroken success, we have

become too self-sufficient to feel the necessity

of redeeming and preserving grace, too proud

to pray to the God that made us.

✎ Full Quote

Write the full quote twice. The first word of each line of the quote is provided.

Intoxicated

become

of

to

Intoxicated

become

of

to

Lesson 25

Name:_____

> When you rise in the morning, give thanks for the light, for your life, for your strength. Give thanks for your food and for the joy of living.
>
> Tecumseh

When you rise in the morning, give thanks for the light, for your life, for your strength. Give thanks for your food and for the joy of living.

✏️ Tracing Practice

Trace the quote twice.

When you rise in the morning, give thanks for the light, for your life, for your strength. Give thanks for your food and for the joy of living.

When you rise in the morning, give thanks for the light, for your life, for your strength. Give thanks for your food and for the joy of living.

54 Aa Bb Cc Dd Ee Ff Gg Hh Ii Jj Kk Ll Mm

✎ Writing Practice

Trace the quote and write it underneath.

When you rise in the morning,

give thanks for the light, for your life,

for your strength. Give thanks for your food

and for the joy of living.

✎ Full Quote

Write the full quote twice. The first word of each line of the quote is provided.

When

give

for

and

When

give

for

and

Lesson 26

How many observe Christ's birthday! How few His precepts!
O! 'tis easier to keep holidays than commandments.

Benjamin Franklin

How many observe Christ's birthday! How
few His precepts! O! 'tis easier to keep
holidays than commandments.

✎ Tracing Practice

Trace the quote twice.

How many observe Christ's birthday! How
few His precepts! O! 'tis easier to keep
holidays than commandments.

How many observe Christ's birthday! How
few His precepts! O! 'tis easier to keep
holidays than commandments.

Aa Bb Cc Dd Ee Ff Gg Hh Ii Jj Kk Ll Mm

✎ Writing Practice

Trace the quote and write it underneath.

How many observe Christ's birthday! How

few His precepts! O! 'tis easier to keep

holidays than commandments.

✎ Full Quote

Write the full quote twice. The first word of each line of the quote is provided.

How

few

holidays

How

few

holidays

Lesson 27

Name: _____

> Freedom is never more than one generation
> away from extinction. We didn't pass it along
> to our children in our bloodstream.
>
> Ronald Reagan

Freedom is never more than one generation
away from extinction. We didn't pass it
along to our children in our bloodstream.

✎ Tracing Practice

Trace the quote twice.

Freedom is never more than one generation
away from extinction. We didn't pass it
along to our children in our bloodstream.

Freedom is never more than one generation
away from extinction. We didn't pass it
along to our children in our bloodstream.

Aa Bb Cc Dd Ee Ff Gg Hh Ii Jj Kk Ll Mm

Trace the quote and write it underneath.

Freedom is never more than one generation

away from extinction. We didn't pass it

along to our children in our bloodstream.

✎ Full Quote

Write the full quote twice. The first word of each line of the quote is provided.

Freedom

away

along

Freedom

away

along

Name: _____

Unless you try to do something
beyond what you have already mastered,
you will never grow.

Unknown

Unless you try to do something
beyond what you have already mastered,
you will never grow.

✏ Tracing Practice

Trace the quote twice.

Unless you try to do something
beyond what you have already mastered,
you will never grow.

Unless you try to do something
beyond what you have already mastered,
you will never grow.

Aa Bb Cc Dd Ee Ff Gg Hh Ii Jj Kk Ll Mm

✎ Writing Practice

Trace the quote and write it underneath.

Unless you try to do something

beyond what you have already mastered,

you will never grow.

✎ Full Quote

Write the full quote twice. The first word of each line of the quote is provided.

Unless

beyond

you

Unless

beyond

you

Name: _____

Our flag honors those who have fought to protect it, and is a reminder of the sacrifice of our nation's founders and heroes.

Joe Barto

Our flag honors those who have fought to protect it, and is a reminder of the sacrifice of our nation's founders and heroes.

✎ Tracing Practice

Trace the quote twice.

Our flag honors those who have fought to protect it, and is a reminder of the sacrifice of our nation's founders and heroes.

Our flag honors those who have fought to protect it, and is a reminder of the sacrifice of our nation's founders and heroes.

Aa Bb Cc Dd Ee Ff Gg Hh Ii Jj Kk Ll Mm

✎ Writing Practice

Trace the quote and write it underneath.

Our flag honors those who have fought

to protect it, and is a reminder of the

sacrifice of our nation's founders and heroes.

✎ Full Quote

Write the full quote twice. The first word of each line of the quote is provided.

Our

to

sacrifice

Our

to

sacrifice

Lesson 30

Name:_____

When the people fear the government, tyranny has found victory.
The federal government is our servant, not our master!

Thomas Jefferson

When the people fear the government, tyranny has found victory. The federal government is our servant, not our master!

✎ Tracing Practice

Trace the quote twice.

When the people fear the government, tyranny has found victory. The federal government is our servant, not our master!

When the people fear the government, tyranny has found victory. The federal government is our servant, not our master!

Aa Bb Cc Dd Ee Ff Gg Hh Ii Jj Kk Ll Mm

✎ Writing Practice

Trace the quote and write it underneath.

When the people fear the government,

tyranny has found victory. The federal

government is our servant, not our master!

✎ Full Quote

Write the full quote twice. The first word of each line of the quote is provided.

When

tyranny

government

When

tyranny

government

Name: _____

> Our contest is not only whether we ourselves shall be free,
> but whether there shall be left to mankind an asylum on earth
> for civil and religious liberty.
>
> Samuel Adams

Our contest is not only whether we ourselves
shall be free, but whether there shall be left
to mankind an asylum on earth
for civil and religious liberty.

✎ Tracing Practice

Trace the quote twice.

Our contest is not only whether we ourselves
shall be free, but whether there shall be left
to mankind an asylum on earth
for civil and religious liberty.

Our contest is not only whether we ourselves
shall be free, but whether there shall be left
to mankind an asylum on earth
for civil and religious liberty.

66 Aa Bb Cc Dd Ee Ff Gg Hh Ii Jj Kk Ll Mm

Trace the quote and write it underneath.

Our contest is not only whether we ourselves

shall be free, but whether there shall be left

to mankind an asylum on earth

for civil and religious liberty.

✎ Full Quote

Write the full quote twice. The first word of each line of the quote is provided.

Our

shall

to

for

Our

shall

to

for

Nn Oo Pp Qq Rr Ss Tt Uu Vv Ww Xx Yy Zz

Lesson 32

> We have no government armed with power capable of contending with human passions unbridled by morality and religion . . .
>
> John Adams

We have no government armed with power capable of contending with human passions unbridled by morality and religion . . .

✐ Tracing Practice

Trace the quote twice.

We have no government armed with power capable of contending with human passions unbridled by morality and religion . . .

We have no government armed with power capable of contending with human passions unbridled by morality and religion . . .

Aa Bb Cc Dd Ee Ff Gg Hh Ii Jj Kk Ll Mm

Trace the quote and write it underneath.

We have no government armed with power

capable of contending with human passions

unbridled by morality and religion . . .

✎ Full Quote

Write the full quote twice. The first word of each line of the quote is provided.

We

capable

unbridled

We

capable

unbridled

Nn Oo Pp Qq Rr Ss Tt Uu Vv Ww Xx Yy Zz

Name:_____

Avarice, ambition, revenge, or gallantry, would break the strongest cords of our Constitution as a whale goes through a net.

John Adams

Avarice, ambition, revenge, or gallantry, would break the strongest cords of our Constitution as a whale goes through the net.

✎ Tracing Practice

Trace the quote twice.

Avarice, ambition, revenge, or gallantry, would break the strongest cords of our Constitution as a whale goes through the net.

Avarice, ambition, revenge, or gallantry, would break the strongest cords of our Constitution as a whale goes through the net.

Aa Bb Cc Dd Ee Ff Gg Hh Ii Jj Kk Ll Mm

Trace the quote and write it underneath.

Avarice, ambition, revenge, or gallantry,

would break the strongest cords of our

Constitution as a whale goes through the net.

✎ Full Quote

Write the full quote twice. The first word of each line of the quote is provided.

Avarice

would

Constitution

Avarice

would

Constitution

Nn Oo Pp Qq Rr Ss Tt Uu Vv Ww Xx Yy Zz   71

Lesson 34

> Our Constitution was made only for a moral and religious people. It is wholly inadequate to the government of any other.
>
> John Adams

Our Constitution was made only for a moral and religious people. It is wholly inadequate to the government of any other.

✎ Tracing Practice

Trace the quote twice.

Our Constitution was made only for a moral and religious people. It is wholly inadequate to the government of any other.

Our Constitution was made only for a moral and religious people. It is wholly inadequate to the government of any other.

Aa Bb Cc Dd Ee Ff Gg Hh Ii Jj Kk Ll Mm

Writing Practice

Trace the quote and write it underneath.

Our Constitution was made only for a

moral and religious people. It is wholly

inadequate to the government of any other.

Full Quote

Write the full quote twice. The first word of each line of the quote is provided.

Our

moral

inadequate

Our

moral

inadequate

Lesson 35

Name: _____

> . . . they therefore who are decrying the Christian religion . . . are undermining the solid foundation of morals, the best security for the duration of free governments.
>
> Charles Carroll, signer of the Declaration of Independence

they therefore who are decrying the Christian religion . . . are undermining the solid foundation of morals, the best security for the duration of free governments.

✎ Tracing Practice

Trace the quote twice.

they therefore who are decrying the Christian religion . . . are undermining the solid foundation of morals, the best security for the duration of free governments.

they therefore who are decrying the Christian religion . . . are undermining the solid foundation of morals, the best security for the duration of free governments.

Aa Bb Cc Dd Ee Ff Gg Hh Ii Jj Kk Ll Mm

Writing Practice

Trace the quote and write it underneath.

they therefore who are decrying the Christian

religion . . . are undermining the solid

foundation of morals, the best security

for the duration of free governments.

Full Quote

Write the full quote twice. The first word of each line of the quote is provided.

they
religion
foundation
for

they
religion
foundation
for

Lesson 36

> Every step we take towards making the State our Caretaker
> of our lives, by that much we move toward
> making the State our Master.
>
> Dwight D. Eisenhower

Every step we take towards making
the State our Caretaker of our lives,
by that much we move toward
making the State our Master.

✏️ Tracing Practice

Trace the quote twice.

Every step we take towards making
the State our Caretaker of our lives,
by that much we move toward
making the State our Master.

Every step we take towards making
the State our Caretaker of our lives,
by that much we move toward
making the State our Master.

Aa Bb Cc Dd Ee Ff Gg Hh Ii Jj Kk Ll Mm

✏️ Writing Practice

Trace the quote and write it underneath.

Every step we take towards making

the State our Caretaker of our lives,

by that much we move toward

making the State our Master.

✏️ Full Quote

Write the full quote twice. The first word of each line of the quote is provided.

Every
the
by
making

Every
the
by
making

Those who would give up essential Liberty, to purchase a little temporary Safety, deserve neither Liberty nor Safety.

Benjamin Franklin

They who would give up an essential
Liberty, to purchase a little temporary
Safety, deserve neither Liberty nor Safety.

✏ Tracing Practice

Trace the quote twice.

They who would give up an essential
Liberty, to purchase a little temporary
Safety, deserve neither Liberty nor Safety.

They who would give up an essential
Liberty, to purchase a little temporary
Safety, deserve neither Liberty nor Safety.

Aa Bb Cc Dd Ee Ff Gg Hh Ii Jj Kk Ll Mm

✎ Writing Practice

Trace the quote and write it underneath.

They who would give up an essential

Liberty, to purchase a little temporary

Safety, deserve neither Liberty nor Safety.

✎ Full Quote

Write the full quote twice. The first word of each line of the quote is provided.

They

Liberty,

Safety,

They

Liberty,

Safety,

Lesson 38

Name:_____

> The Constitution is not an instrument for the government to restrain the people, it is an instrument for the people to restrain the government – lest it come to dominate our lives and interests.
> Patrick Henry

The Constitution is not an instrument
for the government to restrain the people,
it is an instrument for the people
to restrain the government . . .

✎ Tracing Practice

Trace the quote twice.

The Constitution is not an instrument
for the government to restrain the people,
it is an instrument for the people
to restrain the government . . .

The Constitution is not an instrument
for the government to restrain the people,
it is an instrument for the people
to restrain the government . . .

Aa Bb Cc Dd Ee Ff Gg Hh Ii Jj Kk Ll Mm

✎ Writing Practice

Trace the quote and write it underneath.

The Constitution is not an instrument

for the government to restrain the people,

it is an instrument for the people

to restrain the government . . .

✎ Full Quote

Write the full quote twice. The first word of each line of the quote is provided.

The

for

it

to

The

for

it

to

Mm Oo Pp Qq Rr Ss Tt Uu Vv Ww Xx Yy Zz   81

Name:_____

I never . . . believed there was one code of morality
for a public and another for a private man.

Thomas Jefferson

I never . . . believed there was
one code of morality for a public
and another for a private man.

✏ Tracing Practice

Trace the quote twice.

I never . . . believed there was
one code of morality for a public
and another for a private man.

I never . . . believed there was
one code of morality for a public
and another for a private man.

Aa Bb Cc Dd Ee Ff Gg Hh Ii Jj Kk Ll Mm

✎ Writing Practice

Trace the quote and write it underneath.

I never . . . believed there was

one code of morality for a public

and another for a private man.

✎ Full Quote

Write the full quote twice. The first word of each line of the quote is provided.

I

one

and

I

one

and

Name:_____

It is impossible to rightly govern
a nation without God and the Bible.

George Washington

It is impossible to

rightly govern a nation

without God and the Bible.

✎ Tracing Practice

Trace the quote twice.

It is impossible to

rightly govern a nation

without God and the Bible.

It is impossible to

rightly govern a nation

without God and the Bible.

Aa Bb Cc Dd Ee Ff Gg Hh Ii Jj Kk Ll Mm

✎ Writing Practice

Trace the quote and write it underneath.

It is impossible to

rightly govern a nation

without God and the Bible.

✎ Full Quote

Write the full quote twice. The first word of each line of the quote is provided.

It

rightly

without

It

rightly

without

Review Pages

Name: _____

✎ Trace and Copy

My dream is of a place and a time

where America will once again be

seen as the last best hope of earth.

My dream is of a place and a time

where America will once again be

seen as the last best hope of earth.

✎ Write

My

where

seem

Aa Bb Cc Dd Ee Ff Gg Hh Ii Jj Kk Ll Mm

✏ Trace and Copy

Nearly all men can stand adversity

but if you want to test a mans

character, give him power.

Nearly all men can stand adversity

but if you want to test a mans

character, give him power.

✏ Write

Nearly

but

character,

Nn Oo Pp Qq Rr Ss Tt Uu Vv Ww Xx Yy Zz   89

Name:_____

✏ Trace and Copy

Peace cannot be kept by force

it can only be achieved

by understanding.

Peace cannot be kept by force

it can only be achieved

by understanding.

✏ Write

Peace

it

by

Aa Bb Cc Dd Ee Ff Gg Hh Ii Jj Kk Ll Mm

✏ Trace and Copy

Gratitude makes sense of our past,

brings peace for today,

and creates a vision for tomorrow.

Gratitude makes sense of our past,

brings peace for today,

and creates a vision for tomorrow.

✏ Write

Gratitude

brings

and

Nn Oo Pp Qq Rr Ss Tt Uu Vv Ww Xx Yy Zz   91

Review Lesson 5

Name: _____

✎ Trace and Copy

I must trust that the little bit of love

that I sow now will bear many fruits,

here in this world and the life to come.

I must trust that the little bit of love

that I sow now will bear many fruits,

here in this world and the life to come.

✎ Write

I

that

here

Aa Bb Cc Dd Ee Ff Gg Hh Ii Jj Kk Ll Mm

Name: _____

✏ Trace and Copy

Remember that the happiest people

are not those getting more,

but those giving more.

Remember that the happiest people

are not those getting more,

but those giving more.

✏ Write

Remember

are

but

Nn Oo Pp Qq Rr Ss Tt Uu Vv Ww Xx Yy Zz

Review Lesson 7

Name: _____

✏ Trace and Copy

Insanity: doing the same thing

over and over again

and expecting different results.

Insanity: doing the same thing

over and over again

and expecting different results.

✏ Write

Insanity

over

and

94   *Aa Bb Cc Dd Ee Ff Gg Hh Ii Jj Kk Ll Mm*

✎ Trace and Copy

We cannot solve our problems

with the same thinking we used

when we created them.

We cannot solve our problems

with the same thinking we used

when we created them.

✎ Write

We

with

when

Nn Oo Pp Qq Rr Ss Tt Uu Vv Ww Xx Yy Zz   95

Review Lesson 9

Name: _____

✎ Trace and Copy

Try not to become a man

of success, but rather try

to become a man of value.

Try not to become a man

of success, but rather try

to become a man of value.

✎ Write

Try

of

to

Aa Bb Cc Dd Ee Ff Gg Hh Ii Jj Kk Ll Mm

Name: _____

✎ Trace and Copy

To survive in peace and harmony,

united and strong, we must have

one people, one nation, one flag.

To survive in peace and harmony,

united and strong, we must have

one people, one nation, one flag.

✎ Write

To

united

one

Nn Oo Pp Qq Rr Ss Tt Uu Vv Ww Xx Yy Zz

✏ Trace and Copy

A friend is someone

who gives you total freedom

to be yourself.

A friend is someone

who gives you total freedom

to be yourself.

✏ Write

A

who

to

Aa Bb Cc Dd Ee Ff Gg Hh Ii Jj Kk Ll Mm

Name: _____

✏️ Trace and Copy

Love is the only force

capable of transforming

an enemy into a friend.

Love is the only force

capable of transforming

an enemy into a friend.

✏️ Write

Love

capable

an

Nn Oo Pp Qq Rr Ss Tt Uu Vv Ww Xx Yy Zz

Review Lesson 13

Name: _____

✎ Trace and Copy

Our character is what we do

when we think

no one is looking.

Our character is what we do

when we think

no one is looking.

✎ Write

Our

when

no

100 *Aa Bb Cc Dd Ee Ff Gg Hh Ii Jj Kk Ll Mm*

✎ Trace and Copy

Always do your best.

What you plant now,

you will harvest later.

Always do your best.

What you plant now,

you will harvest later.

✎ Write

Always

What

you

Nn Oo Pp Qq Rr Ss Tt Uu Vv Ww Xx Yy Zz   101

✏ Trace and Copy

Better to remain silent and be

thought a fool than to speak out

and remove all doubt.

Better to remain silent and be

thought a fool than to speak out

and remove all doubt.

✏ Write

Better

thought

and

Aa Bb Cc Dd Ee Ff Gg Hh Ii Jj Kk Ll Mm

✎ Trace and Copy

Success is not final, failure

is not fatal: it is the courage

to continue that counts.

Success is not final, failure

is not fatal: it is the courage

to continue that counts.

✎ Write

Success

is

to

Nn Oo Pp Qq Rr Ss Tt Uu Vv Ww Xx Yy Zz   103

✎ Trace and Copy

Coming together is a beginning;

keeping together is progress;

working together is success.

Coming together is a beginning;

keeping together is progress;

working together is success.

✎ Write

Coming

keeping

working

Aa Bb Cc Dd Ee Ff Gg Hh Ii Jj Kk Ll Mm

✎ Trace and Copy

Perfection is not attainable,

but if we chase perfection

we can catch excellence.

Perfection is not attainable,

but if we chase perfection

we can catch excellence.

✎ Write

Perfection

but

we

Nn Oo Pp Qq Rr Ss Tt Uu Vv Ww Xx Yy Zz   105

Review Lesson 19

Name: _____

✏️ Trace and Copy

Live so that when your children

think of fairness, caring and integrity,

they think of you.

Live so that when your children

think of fairness, caring and integrity,

they think of you.

✏️ Write

Live

think

they

Aa Bb Cc Dd Ee Ff Gg Hh Ii Jj Kk Ll Mm

Trace and Copy

It is easier to build

strong children than

to repair broken men.

It is easier to build

strong children than

to repair broken men.

Write

It

strong

to

Nn Oo Pp Qq Rr Ss Tt Uu Vv Ww Xx Yy Zz   107

Name: _____

✎ Trace and Copy

If we ever forget that we are

One Nation Under God, then we

will be a nation gone under.

If we ever forget that we are

One Nation Under God, then we

will be a nation gone under.

✎ Write

If

One

will

Aa Bb Cc Dd Ee Ff Gg Hh Ii Jj Kk Ll Mm

Review Lesson 22

Name:_____

Trace and Copy

Every human has four endowments --

self--awareness, conscience, independent

will, and creative imagination.

Every human has four endowments --

self--awareness, conscience, independent

will, and creative imagination.

Write

Every

self--

will,

Nn Oo Pp Qq Rr Ss Tt Uu Vv Ww Xx Yy Zz

Name:_____

✏️ Trace and Copy

Life is ten percent what happens

to you and ninety percent

how you react to it.

Life is ten percent what happens

to you and ninety percent

how you react to it.

✏️ Write

Life

to

how

Aa Bb Cc Dd Ee Ff Gg Hh Ii Jj Kk Ll Mm

✎ Trace and Copy

Intoxicated with unbroken success, we have

become too self-sufficient to feel the necessity

of redeeming and preserving grace, too proud

to pray to the God that made us.

Intoxicated with unbroken success, we have

become too self-sufficient to feel the necessity

of redeeming and preserving grace, too proud

to pray to the God that made us.

✎ Write

Intoxicated

become

of

to

Nn Oo Pp Qq Rr Ss Tt Uu Vv Ww Xx Yy Zz   *111*

Review Lesson 25

✏ Trace and Copy

When you rise in the morning,

give thanks for the light, for your life,

for your strength. Give thanks for your food

and for the joy of living.

When you rise in the morning,

give thanks for the light, for your life,

for your strength. Give thanks for your food

and for the joy of living.

✏ Write

When

give

for

and

Aa Bb Cc Dd Ee Ff Gg Hh Ii Jj Kk Ll Mm

Name: _____

✎ Trace and Copy

How many observe Christ's birthday! How

few His precepts! O! 'tis easier to keep

holidays than commandments.

How many observe Christ's birthday! How

few His precepts! O! 'tis easier to keep

holidays than commandments.

✎ Write

How

few

holidays

Nn Oo Pp Qq Rr Ss Tt Uu Vv Ww Xx Yy Zz   113

Review Lesson 27   Name:_____

✏️ Trace and Copy

Freedom is never more than one generation

away from extinction. We didn't pass it

along to our children in our bloodstream.

Freedom is never more than one generation

away from extinction. We didn't pass it

along to our children in our bloodstream.

✏️ Write

Freedom

away

along

Aa Bb Cc Dd Ee Ff Gg Hh Ii Jj Kk Ll Mm

Review Lesson 28

✎ Trace and Copy

Unless you try to do something

beyond what you have already mastered,

you will never grow.

Unless you try to do something

beyond what you have already mastered,

you will never grow.

✎ Write

Unless

beyond

you

Nn Oo Pp Qq Rr Ss Tt Uu Vv Ww Xx Yy Zz

Name:_____

✎ Trace and Copy

Our flag honors those who have fought

to protect it, and is a reminder of the

sacrifice of our nations' founders and heroes.

Our flag honors those who have fought

to protect it, and is a reminder of the

sacrifice of our nations' founders and heroes.

✎ Write

Our

to

sacrifice

Aa Bb Cc Dd Ee Ff Gg Hh Ii Jj Kk Ll Mm

Name: _____

✎ Trace and Copy

When the people fear the government,

tyranny has found victory. The federal

government is our servant, not our master!

When the people fear the government,

tyranny has found victory. The federal

government is our servant, not our master!

✎ Write

When

tyranny

government

Nn Oo Pp Qq Rr Ss Tt Uu Vv Ww Xx Yy Zz   117

✎ Trace and Copy

Our contest is not only whether we ourselves

shall be free, but whether there shall be left

to mankind an asylum on earth

for civil and religious liberty.

Our contest is not only whether we ourselves

shall be free, but whether there shall be left

to mankind an asylum on earth

for civil and religious liberty.

✎ Write

Our

shall

to

for

Aa Bb Cc Dd Ee Ff Gg Hh Ii Jj Kk Ll Mm

✎ Trace and Copy

We have no government armed with power

capable of contending with human passions

unbridled by morality and religion . . .

We have no government armed with power

capable of contending with human passions

unbridled by morality and religion . . .

✎ Write

We

capable

unbridled

Nn Oo Pp Qq Rr Ss Tt Uu Vv Ww Xx Yy Zz   119

Name: _____

✎ Trace and Copy

Avarice, ambition, revenge, or gallantry,

would break the strongest cords of our

Constitution as a whale goes through the net.

Avarice, ambition, revenge, or gallantry,

would break the strongest cords of our

Constitution as a whale goes through the net.

✎ Write

Avarice

would

Constitution

Aa Bb Cc Dd Ee Ff Gg Hh Ii Jj Kk Ll Mm

Review Lesson 34

Name: _____

✎ Trace and Copy

Our Constitution was made only for a

moral and religious people. It is wholly

inadequate to the government of any other.

Our Constitution was made only for a

moral and religious people. It is wholly

inadequate to the government of any other.

✎ Write

Our

moral

inadequate

Nn Oo Pp Qq Rr Ss Tt Uu Vv Ww Xx Yy Zz

✎ Trace and Copy

they therefore who are decrying the Christian

religion . . . are undermining the solid

foundation of morals, the best security

for the duration of free governments.

they therefore who are decrying the Christian

religion . . . are undermining the solid

foundation of morals, the best security

for the duration of free governments.

✎ Write

they

religion

foundation

for

Aa Bb Cc Dd Ee Ff Gg Hh Ii Jj Kk Ll Mm

✎ Trace and Copy

Every step we take towards making

the State our Caretaker of our lives,

by that much we move toward

making the State our Master.

Every step we take towards making

the State our Caretaker of our lives,

by that much we move toward

making the State our Master.

✎ Write

Every

the

by

making

Nn Oo Pp Qq Rr Ss Tt Uu Vv Ww Xx Yy Zz   123

Review Lesson 37   Name: _____

✎ Trace and Copy

They who would give up an essential

Liberty, to purchase a little temporary

Safety, deserve neither Liberty nor Safety.

They who would give up an essential

Liberty, to purchase a little temporary

Safety, deserve neither Liberty nor Safety.

✎ Write

They

Liberty,

Safety,

Aa Bb Cc Dd Ee Ff Gg Hh Ii Jj Kk Ll Mm

✎ Trace and Copy

The Constitution is not an instrument

for the government to restrain the people,

it is an instrument for the people

to restrain the government . . .

The Constitution is not an instrument

for the government to restrain the people,

it is an instrument for the people

to restrain the government . . .

✎ Write

The

for

it

to

Nn Oo Pp Qq Rr Ss Tt Uu Vv Ww Xx Yy Zz   /25

✎ Trace and Copy

I never . . . believed there was

one code of morality for a public

and another for a private man.

I never . . . believed there was

one code of morality for a public

and another for a private man.

✎ Write

I

one

and

Aa Bb Cc Dd Ee Ff Gg Hh Ii Jj Kk Ll Mm

✎ Trace and Copy

It is impossible to

rightly govern a nation

without God and the Bible.

It is impossible to

rightly govern a nation

without God and the Bible.

✎ Write

It

rightly

without

Nn Oo Pp Qq Rr Ss Tt Uu Vv Ww Xx Yy Zz

Items available from Laurelwood Books:

Ōlim, Once Upon a Time, in Latin Series:
(Supplementary audio files available for all Latin titles)

Book I (reader and workbook): The Three Little Pigs,
The Tortoise and the Hare, The Crow and the Pitcher

Book II (reader and workbook): The Ant and the Chrysalis,
The Lost Sheep, The Good Samaritan

Book III (reader and workbook) - The Feeding of the 5,000,
The Lion and the Mouse

Book IV (reader and workbook) - Creation

Book V (reader and workbook) - Daniel, Part I; We Know a Tree by its Fruit

Book VI (reader and workbook) - The Prodigal Son

Book VII (reader and workbook) - David and Goliath

Book VIII (reader and workbook) - Daniel, Part II

Book IX (reader and workbook) - Daniel, Part III, The Miser

Book X (reader and workbook) - The Wise Man and Foolish Man,
The Ten Maidens

Ōlim Derivatives I
Ōlim Derivatives II
Latin Verbs: To Infinitives and Beyond! Book I & II

Scripture Scribes Series
Pre-Primary: *From Scribbler to Scribe*
Primary: *Who Made Me?, My Whole Heart, His Name Is Wonderful,*
Psalms & Proverbs for Young Catholics, Practicing Proverbs
Intermediate: *One Another, Savoring Psalms*
Upper School: *Men of Honor & Women of Grace, Walking With God*

Items available from Laurelwood Books:

Patriotic Penmanship Series for Grades K-12

Also Available:
Jump Rope Review Book
Transition to Cursive Book
Dinosaurs From A to Z Review Book

State The Facts: A Guide to Studying Your State

Whether you are studying the state you live in or any other state,
this book offers your student the opportunity to research
and learn state history, geography, weather, and more!

Study Guides

Based on Rosemary Sutcliff's historical fiction:

The Eagle of the Ninth
The Silver Branch
Outcast
The Lantern Bearers
Warrior Scarlet
Sword Song
The Shining Company

Based on Emma Leslie's historical fiction:

Out of the Mouth of the Lion
Glaucia the Greek Slave

Laurelwood Books offers both new and used curricula to families wishing
to help their children learn and achieve success in school or at home.

To order: www.laurelwoodbooks.com
marylnw7@gmail.com